'*Cherry Orchard*' *designed by Paul Nash, block-printed in black, grey and cream. The print was originally produced by Footprints, the fashionable interior decorators run by Mrs Eric Kennington, which opened in Beauchamp Place, London, in the late 1920s. In 1930-1 G. P. and J. Baker Ltd printed the design on silk for Cresta Silks Ltd of Welwyn Garden City, a company which used avante-garde artists to design fabrics for manufacture into garments for retail through their own chain of shops.*

COVER: *A textile block printer assisted by his helper, the '*tierer*', who provides a continuous supply of colour from which the block is recharged after each application.*

TEXTILE PRINTING

Hazel Clark

Shire Publications Ltd

CONTENTS

Copyright © 1985 by Hazel Clark. First published 1985. Shire Album 135 ISBN 0 85263 729 2.

British Library Cataloguing in Publication data available.

Set in 9 point Times roman and printed in Great Britain by C. I. Thomas & Sons (Haverfordwest) Ltd, Press Buildings, Merlins Bridge, Haverfordwest, Dyfed.

Nineteenth-century printed textile designs in watercolour on paper.

Late fourteenth to early fifteenth-century woodblock print in black on pink linen, probably Flemish, which appears to depict bird snaring scenes.

EUROPEAN ORIGINS

The patterning of fabric, by applying surface colour, originated somewhere in Asia. There are records of Indian printed fabrics being found in ancient Greece and Rome. Printed cloths were also known in Byzantium. The earliest known technique, block printing, probably originated with the Chinese, who were letterpress-printing paper by woodblock two thousand years ago. In Europe printed textiles came comparatively late, initially as poor competitors to woven silks.

The Lower Rhineland region of Germany was probably one of the first parts of Europe to produce printed textiles. Between the tenth and fourteenth centuries block printing was being carried on in monasteries, which were then centres for arts and learning, as a craft activity. It was not until the Renaissance that it became a commercial venture practised in towns.

Design inspiration came from the precious patterned silks and velvets which were being transported along the Rhine from the orient, Italy and Sicily. Various means were employed to try to imitate their sumptuous quality. Silk and linen were printed with sticky black paint, on to which was sprinkled powdered glass, gold and silver in futile attempts to rival the originals. The patterns were quite primitive, usually printed with small woodblocks applied repeatedly to a plain background. Meanwhile in other European countries single-coloured designs were being printed using larger blocks on simple linen canvas, often with the addition of hand-painted details. Some textile printing was being carried on in the Netherlands and France during the middle ages, but Italy was the other principal exponent at the time.

By the fourteenth century Italy was already an established centre of silk weaving. From Venice, an important link with the trade routes from the east, came knowledge of techniques and designs. Block printing, which was practised in Italian cities during the Renaissance, proved an alternative means of decorating fabric. The artist Cennino Cennini mentioned it in his *Treatise on Painting* written in the late fourteenth or early

LEFT: *The 'pomegranate' motif, from a detail of a painted and dyed cotton gown. The print was produced in the northern region of the Indian Coromandel coast, in the first quarter of the eighteenth century, for the European (Dutch) market.*
RIGHT: *A panel of fine white cotton, measuring 48 inches (1220 mm) by 14 inches (355 mm), hand-painted in India. Delicately and freely drawn blue stems and leaves combine with red and purple flowers to surround the male figure, with his wings of purple and red, in the centre. The various large and small birds are painted in shades of red and blue and the little dog is purple. Patterns of this type inspired European printers to attempt to reproduce their colour quality and adapt their motifs to suit western taste.*

fifteenth century. He recommended that black designs should be applied to green, red, yellow or dark blue cloth, with any details required being provided by hand using a brush. The resulting fabrics, he felt, were 'good for children's and youths' clothing and lectern cloths', not as competition for silks and velvets. The printers belonged to the same guilds as painters, having more in common with them than with the weavers. In Italy printing was an inferior alternative to weaving, whereas in Germany it was considered a potential substitute. In spite of these differences in intention, throughout the middle ages designs were derived from woven textiles and thus developed in a similar manner across Europe.

The earliest surviving European examples of printed fabric, dating from the twelfth to the fourteenth centuries, showing flat heraldic birds and animals next to stylised trees, closely resemble patterns from Byzantine and Sicilian textiles. The

4

A cotton head covering, polychrome block-printed in Genoa, northern Italy, imitating an Indian design. The so called 'Tree of Life', a symbolic image common on Indian painted and printed palampores (hangings), was freely adapted for European chintz.

subsequent appearance of more elaborate animals and birds, monsters, architectural and floral motifs has been linked with Siennese, Lucan and Florentine weaves of the fourteenth and early fifteenth centuries. Pictorials, especially religious scenes from the New Testament, inspired by silks, bring to mind the wood-engraved images being printed on parchment and paper from about 1450. At the same time the so called 'pomegranate' motif, seen on Italian silks and velvets but originating in the east, became widespread as a printed pattern. Increased output by the European silk industry during the following century led to a decline in the production of printed textiles. For over a century the skill lay dormant, only to be revived as a result of the influx of Indian printed and painted cottons into Europe.

The voyages of merchant adventurers to the islands of the South China Sea in search of spices brought the knowledge of Indian chintzes to the west. In the opening years of the seventeenth century England and Holland followed Spain and Portugal in setting up East India Companies to establish their trade legally. The much sought-after spices could not simply be purchased from the islanders. Nutmegs, peppers, ginger and the like had to be bartered with painted fabrics, which were picked up on the way south, from the Coromandel coast in south-east India. Some of these cloths were brought back to Europe, where their bright fast colours made them, together with elephants' teeth and porcelain vessels, into desirable curiosities. It was not long before designs were being sent out to India in order to make the native patterns more acceptable to the western eye. The growth in popularity of these colourful chintzes encouraged European printers to try to emulate them.

A detail from 'Les Travaux de la Manufacture', one of the most famous copperplate prints produced at C. P. Oberkampf's Jouy works in 1783-4, showing all the stages from preparing the cloth to finishing the printed fabric. In this fragment two men are using a flat bed copperplate press from which the printed fabric, bearing a crest and the inscription 'Manufacture Royale De C P Oberkampf' emerges on top to be carried to the drying frame overhead.

COPPERPLATE PRINTING

Modern textile printing using fast colourful dyes was introduced into Europe during the last quarter of the seventeenth century. The first successful attempts to imitate the Indian imports seem to have occurred simultaneously in England, France and Holland around 1670. An engraver, William Sherwin, who in 1676 took out a patent for 'a new way of printing broad callicoe', established the first English printworks on the river Lea at West Ham, in east London. By the end of the century the industry was well established and works were also to be found at Hackney, Stepney, Spitalfields and Bow. Even at this early stage the weavers, fearing competition, put pressure on the British government to impose sanctions on printed calicoes.

In 1700, the government passed an Act forbidding the importation of Indian, Persian and Chinese printed calicoes. The Act misfired by providing a stimulus to the home printers. Next, in 1712 and 1714, heavy excise duties were placed on home-printed cloths. A final Act, in 1720, prohibited the printing of all-cotton cloths, with the exception of fustian, a coarse fabric with a linen warp and a cotton weft. None of these Acts totally prevented cloth being printed, although they undoubtedly restricted its development. In 1774, recognising that the injunctions had failed to curb the demand for prints, the government lifted the prohibitions and replaced them with a series of excise duties, which lasted until 1831.

The early textiles were printed by woodblocks, but during the later years of

A detail of a plate print showing classical and pastoral scenes, in crimson on a white cotton, printed by Robert Jones of Old Ford, near Poplar, Essex, in 1761 and inscribed, 'R. I. & Co Old Ford 1761' and 'R Iones 1761'. The peacock is from a 1740 engraving by Josephus Sympson of London, after the painting by Marmaduke Cradock. The print also includes a pastoral scene from an etching by Nicholas Berchem in 1652 and a stag and a dog from page 18 of 'Animals of Various Species Accurately Drawn by Francis Barlow'. This is one of the earliest and finest surviving plate prints.

prohibition copperplate printing was introduced from Ireland. This intaglio technique enabled large finely drawn images to be printed from flat hand-engraved metal plates measuring from under a foot to a yard square (300 mm to 910 mm). Both in technique and appearance they closely resembled engraved book illustra-

tions, which, with paintings, provided the engraver with a virtually inexhaustible source of inspiration.

Typical patterns were florals and pictorial scenes depicting figures, landscapes, classical ruins, contemporary and theatrical events. The process was best suited to isolated images rather than to repeats, which were never technically perfect. Similar pictorials appeared as transfer prints on ceramics and enamels, the same engravers often being associated with both industries. Copperplate prints could be produced only in a single colour, which for textiles was most usually black, sepia, blue, purple or crimson. Any flat areas of colour had to be 'pencilled' (painted) in by hand using a fine brush.

The years between 1760 and 1785 have been referred to as the golden age of London copperplate printing. At the same time in France the prints produced at C. P. Oberkampf's works at Jouy, south-west of Paris, had an equally high reputation. The printworks, which was often visited by Marie Antoinette and her court, gave the name *toiles de Jouy* to French copperplate-printed textiles. Originally popular for ladies' dresses, in both countries the fabrics were used increasingly for furnishings after the mid eighteenth century.

While copperplates could produce fine linear and tonal effects, the method was nevertheless limited in terms of colour. During the early years of the nineteenth century its use declined and by the 1830s it was virtually obsolete. After this time it continued to be used only for commemorative handkerchiefs and squares. Its demise was symptomatic of changes in the industry, which by 1800 had moved its geographical centre away from London to Lancashire.

A commemorative handkerchief plate showing the exterior of the Great Exhibition of 1851. A companion exists of the interior, depicting the central nave.

8

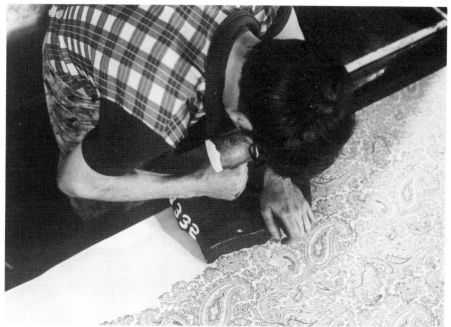

The block printer uses the wooden handle, rather than the leaden head, of his 'maul' to give an even pressure. During a nine-hour shift he would be capable of producing approximately 125 yards (114 metres) of fabric in one colour. When printing three colours his output would be reduced to 60 yards (54 metres) and further reduced to 45 yards (41 metres) for a four-colour design.

BLOCK PRINTING

During the short-lived fashion for copperplates, block prints were still produced as they had been for centuries. Few plate prints issued from the newly established Lancashire printworks, where the initial emphasis was on colourful polychrome block-printed dress and furnishing fabric. The technique employed, which differed little from that used in the past, continued into the twentieth century.

Block printing is a method where an image is applied to fabric from a raised (relief) surface. The blocks comprise several layers of wood glued together with the grain running in different directions, the uppermost layer being hardwood. A variety of printed effects can be achieved by creating the relief image on the blocks in different ways, one of which is cutting directly into the wood. A second method is *coppering*, whereby the application of copper or brass strips and

pins to the block can give linear and stipple effects reminiscent of copperplate prints. Another effect is *felting*, where thick felt soaked in water and gum is recessed into the block surface. This technique is often applied to *colour blocks*, which are used to print areas requiring heavier colour deposits.

In printing, one block is needed for each colour; thus the total number of blocks depends on the design. The fabric is printed with a colour which must dry before the next one can be put on top. Blocks must be carefully cut and shaped in order that the printed images relate to one another both vertically and horizontally. The maximum block dimensions are approximately 18 inches (460 mm) square and 2½ inches (60 mm) deep. Anything greater, or weighing more than 10 pounds (4.5 kg), would be too heavy for the printer to handle comfortably.

Traditionally the block printer always

9

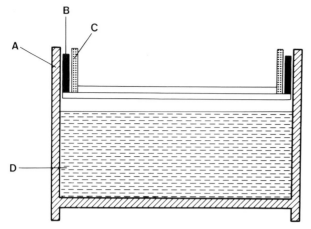

LEFT: *The block printer's sieve and 'swimming tub'. The diagram shows: A, the wooden tub; B, a drum with a waterproof covering, floating freely on the surface of the tub's contents; C, a drum, or sieve, stretched with fine woollen cloth, on to which the printing colour is brushed (a separate sieve is required for each colour, but the same swimming tub can be used); D, old colour or dye paste.*

RIGHT: *One of the blocks used to print the 'Evenlode' chintz designed by William Morris in 1883. The block is made of wood with 'felting' in the larger areas. The metal 'pitch' pins protruding from the corners are used to position (register) the block accurately.*

10

Building up an image using four wood-blocks, each one printing a different colour. From W. J. Crookes, 'A Practical Handbook of Dyeing and Calico Printing', 1874.

had his own helper, or *tierer,* usually a young boy or a woman. The tierer's responsiblity was to provide an even layer of colour, from which the printer replenished his block after each application. The colour was brushed on to a sieve, essentially a woollen blanket stretched over a tub of used gum (a constituent of the printing colour), serving as a springy pad and contained in a *swimming tub* on a *print carriage* which ran alongside the table. Once furnished with colour, the block was printed on to cloth which was stretched and fixed firmly, by a hot iron, to the gummed surface along the length of a sturdy table, already covered with a resilient blanket and waterproof topping. Firm pressure from the printer's hammer, known as a *maul,* was applied additionally to transfer the image to heavyweight and coarse fabrics.

The advantage of block printing is that it can provide highly coloured, complex patterns and be used for short runs of exclusive designs. However, it is a very time-consuming and labour-expensive

technique. Increased demand for fashionable fabrics, principally for ladies' dresses, first apparent in the early decades of the nineteenth century, stimulated attempts to speed the process. This was particularly so in France, where block printing continued to be more widely used than in Britain.

The surface printing machine, invented by the Frenchman, Ebinger in 1800, was intended to compete with the speed of the Lancashire cylinder machines (see next chapter). The wooden rollers used in the process created initial problems: being as wide as the cloth and several inches thick, they tended to warp when in prolonged contact with wet colour. The introduction of coppering and felting and the application of waterproof varnish to the non-printing areas helped to overcome this. During the early nineteenth century Lancashire printers used surface rollers and copper cylinders together in the aptly named *union* or *mule* machines. In Britain the technique was never popular for textiles, but it was used for printing wallpaper and linoleum.

11

Another notable French invention was the *Perrotine*, a block-printing machine, patented by M Perrot of Rouen in 1834. It mechanised the process by using blocks which were as long as the width of the fabric but only 3 to 5¼ inches (76 to 130 mm) wide. Through the successive printing of one block over another with a different colour, the fabric which left the machine was completely printed ready for finishing.

Perrotines were restricted to producing small repeats of the same depth as the blocks and were therefore unsuitable for furnishing fabrics, which by the 1830s were the mainstay of the British block trade. They did, however, improve upon the output of the hand block printer by over 200 per cent and were well used in France. They were not very popular in Britain as cylinder printing had already begun to be influential before Perrotines were introduced. Elsewhere in Europe they continued in operation until the 1960s.

Around the middle of the nineteenth century the introduction of *cast* or *stereotype blocks* speeded blockmaking and created a more durable printing

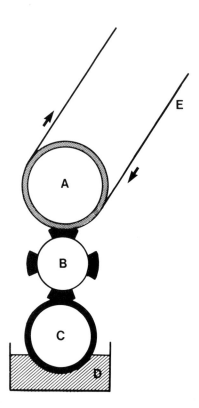

ABOVE: *Ebinger's surface printing machine of 1834: A, the pressure cylinder wrapped with thick cotton lapping; B, the wooden printing roller cut in relief with a design (its peg-like appearance in cross-section was responsible for this also being known as the 'peg' machine); C, the colour furnishing roller with a cloth wrapping; D, the colour box; E, the fabric to be printed.*

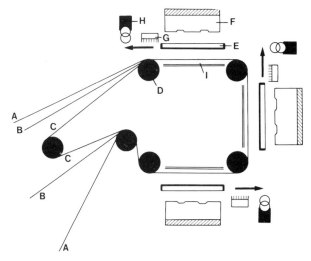

LEFT: *The Perrotine: A, the fabric to be printed; B, the cotton 'back grey' fabric; C, an endless blanket; D, four rollers carrying the blanket; E, the colour sieve, which moves to one side when the block has been furnished with dye to enable the block to print the fabric; F, the printing block; G, the brush, which smoothes colour on the sieve; H, the colour furnishing rollers in the colour box; I, the cast iron table.*

RIGHT: *The printer furnishing his block from the colour sieve contained in the 'print carriage' which runs alongside the table.*

BELOW: *Wooden surface rollers which have been 'felted', 'coppered' and varnished on the non-printing areas.*

13

surface. The stereotype cast plates were produced from separate wooden casting moulds cut with a gas-heated (later electrically heated) mechanical device which burned the design image into the wood. This provided a mould into which lead type metal was poured. The resulting cast was then attached to the surface of the laminated block ready for printing. A number of stereotypes could be fixed to the same block in order to print an all-over or border pattern. These hard-wearing blocks were particularly appropriate for Perrotine machines and 'impact' printing, introduced in the 1940s.

In spite of these inventions, block printing could no longer retain its commercial supremacy beyond the first half of the nineteenth century. It was unable to compete in the growing mass market, which increasingly demanded quantity rather than high quality. As a craft activity and for superior furnishings, block printing has nevertheless survived in a considerably diminished form to the present.

The revived interest in crafts in the later nineteenth century, especially the work of William Morris and his colleagues, aided the survival of block work. In the 1930s the efforts of Phyllis Barron and Dorothy Larcher helped to keep the skill alive. Today Susan Boscence continues this tradition from her Devon workshop. Commercially, the technique is virtually obsolete in Britain, but elsewhere in the world, notably in India, it continues to be economically viable. For wallpaper, Sandersons still use Morris woodblocks at their Perivale works near London to produce a small amount of paper, retailed at a high price that depends on the number of colours involved.

RIGHT: *'Brother Rabbit'* designed by William Morris in 1882, a block print using the ancient indigo discharge method revived by Morris. The natural indigo dye cannot be printed directly on to the cloth because of oxidisation when exposed to air. The fabric is therefore dyed and then printed with a bleaching reagent, which reduces the design to a half-tone.

BELOW: *A woman with an 'impact' printing machine at David Evans Printworks, Crayford, Kent, in 1979. The machines were introduced at the works in the early 1950s to speed up block printing. The block was clamped into the machine, which ran along rails at either side of the table, and, by a series of levers and locks, was 'impacted' on to the fabric. At its most efficient impact printing was fifty per cent quicker than hand block work.*

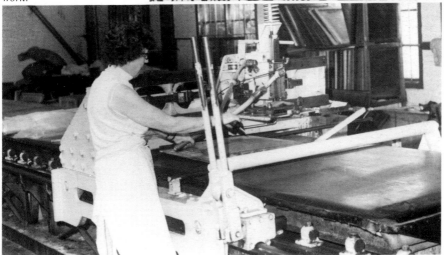

ABOVE: *Phyllis Barron and Dorothy Larcher's workshop at Painswick, Gloucestershire, about 1935. The acquisition of a set of old French woodblocks inspired Barron's interest in block printing. Together, the two women soon learned enough of the process to make their own blocks, dyestuffs and other intricate pieces of equipment, including a basket steamer.*

LEFT: *'Elizabethan', a woodblock cut by Phyllis Barron and hand-printed in galled iron on natural linen. The design was first cut by Barron in 1925 to print furnishing materials for the Duke of Westminster's daughter's coming-out dance. In the 1920s and 1930s such designs were much sought after for fashionable 'modernistic' interiors.*

16

CYLINDER PRINTING

In 1783 a Scotsman, Thomas Bell, patented the cylinder machine, which was to change the whole nature of textile printing. Although not the first of its type, Bell's machine incorporated a metal *doctor* blade which scraped excess colour from the rollers (the word 'doctor' probably deriving from 'abductor').

Initially the cylinders were made of solid copper, but *shell* or copper-faced rollers, which were cheaper to produce and lighter to handle, later proved a successful alternative. They were intaglio-engraved like copperplates and each cylinder printed one colour. At first only three or four cylinders could be combined in a printing machine, but this increased to as many as fourteen in the twentieth century. Depending on the job, the cylinders could be between 32 and 80 inches (810 and 2030 mm) wide with diameters from 5 to 30 inches (127 to 760 mm). Few machines could produce more than a 36 inch (910 mm) vertical repeat, but sizes larger than this were very rarely required.

Although invented for use in conjunction with hand blocks, by the 1830s cylinder printing was gaining predominance as a technique in its own right. Powered by water, steam and eventually electricity, the machines helped to increase considerably the output of printed fabric. Exports to places as far apart as China and South America burgeoned. In Britain the working classes were able to afford colourful patterned fabric for the first time. Because of the new machines and the lifting of the excise duty in 1831, a 'useful and respectable' printed dress, which previously would have cost 4 shillings could now be bought for 2s 6d.

The Lancashire printers had eagerly adopted the new machines, which brought them greater profits than other methods. Like woodblocks, the cylinders were originally engraved by hand, but increased production quickly led to the introduction of machine engraving.

The *mill and die* engraving method introduced in the early nineteenth century by the Manchester engravers Joseph Lockett and Company was particularly successful. A small cylindrical steel *die*, about 3 inches (76 mm) long and 1 inch (25 mm) thick, was hand-engraved with a motif. It was then hardened and tempered before being rotated under pressure against a larger softened cylindrical steel *mill*, which accepted the pattern in relief. The mill was then hardened to

Cylinder printing, from the 'Cyclopaedia of Useful Arts, Mechanical and Chemical, Manufacturers, Mining and Engineering', Volume I, 1854.

LEFT: *A twelve-colour cylinder printing machine manufactured by Mather and Platt of Manchester, one of the major suppliers of textile machinery, around 1910.*

BELOW: *A late eighteenth-century French polychrome with a roller-printed outline in red, block-printed yellows, browns and dull green on buff. The figures by the chicken coop are taken from an engraving after a painting by J. R. Russell, RA, dated 1788. This rustic scene is very similar to a group of monochrome pictorials which were roller-printed around 1820.*

18

A 4 inch (100 mm) long 'die' engraved with a design which will be transferred in relief to a 'mill' ready for engraving a copper cylinder.

make it ready for engraving a roller by being mechanically rotated around the surface as many times as necessary. This procedure speeded up engraving while making available many designs which had previously been too expensive or complicated to engrave by hand. Once engraved, the dies were retained for future use in different combinations, to produce new designs.

Pentagraph engraving was another mechanical method which saved time by transferring an image from a flat engraved zinc plate on to the prepared surface of the cylinder. In so doing it repeated and enlarged the pattern, traditionally five times (although the word 'pentagraph' is a corruption of 'pantograph'). The cylinder was covered with varnish and the pattern transferred using diamond-pointed styluses which laid bare the copper ready for *etching* with nitric acid. Such processes did not make obsolete the skills of the hand engravers, who were still needed for making corrections and alterations.

A sample of a 'mill' design printed on paper by Lockett, Crossland and Company, one of the leading Manchester specialist engraving firms during the early nineteenth century.

ABOVE: *Painting out areas of the roller prior to etching. From W. J. Crookes, 'A Practical Handbook of Dyeing and Calico Printing', 1874.*

BELOW, LEFT: *A single-colour cylinder printing machine: A, the pressure cylinder wrapped in thick lapping; B, the engraved copper cylinder; C, the colour furnishing roller; D, the colour box; E, the 'lint doctor' which removes any impurities the cylinder has picked up from the cloth; F, the metal doctor blade, which scrapes excess colour from the cylinder; G, rollers; H, the fabric to be printed; I, the cotton 'back grey' (which protects the blanket from staining); J, the endless blanket.*

BELOW, RIGHT: *The Stork rotary screen printing machine (cross-section of one screen): A, the finely perforated nickel screen; B, the central colour supply shaft; C, the printing colour; D, the flexible steel squeegee; E, the fabric adhered to the printing table.*

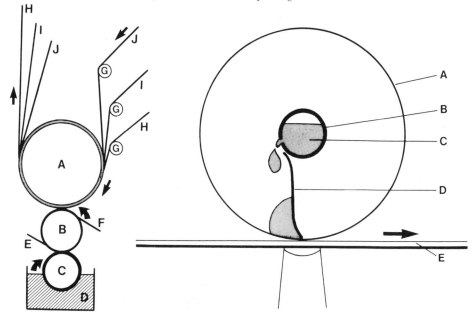

20

During the 1920s and 1930s the first experiments were made to 'engrave' cylinders photographically, but it was not until the late 1950s that this became established practice in Britain. (The method involved etching, but the trade continued to use the old terminology.) Even then, mechanical methods were preferable for some work, such as very small repeating patterns. Around the same time, cylinders were chromium-plated after engraving to enable each one to print as much as 100,000 yards (91,000 metres) more.

It was in the printing of large quantities of fabric that cylinder machines continued to excel until the late 1960s. During the 1970s they began to suffer a similar challenge to that which they had once posed to block printing. In the 1980s cylinder printing machines are still in operation in the east but they have become scarce in the west, where other faster and cheaper methods have taken over. Brunschweiler (UK) Ltd of Manchester is one of the few firms to retain the method, as the most convenient means of printing the hot-wax batiks which it exports chiefly to West Africa. Once more the effects of new technology, combined with changes in market demands, have influenced textile printing.

SILKSCREEN PRINTING

In simple terms, screen printing is based on stencilling, a technique which originated long ago in the Far East and was perfected in Japan. It was introduced to European textile printing in the late nineteenth century, but it was not until the 1920s and 1930s that its commercial potential was realised. Since then, flat and subsequently rotary screens have become predominant in the industry.

FLAT-SCREEN PRINTING

Flat screens have provided the opportunity for shorter print runs and greater variety in design. For manufacturers the process has the advantage that screens are cheap to produce and do not need skilled labour to use.

The screens are shallow trays consisting of a wooden or, for greater durability, a metal frame stretched with 'silk' (nylon or polyester). The design is applied to it by masking those areas through which the printing colour is not intended to pass. (Originally this was done using varnish, but photochemical techniques are now used commercially.) Dye is forced through the screen by the application of pressure from a *squeegee*, a wedge-shaped wooden bar, usually with a rubber edge. Printing takes place on tables not dissimilar to those used in block printing (measuring about 54 yards, 50 metres,

A large metal-framed screen being stretched with 'silk', using hydraulic pressure.

Hand screen printing, 1979.

long for hand and semi-automatic screen printing, as compared with approximately 10 yards, 9.1 m, for a block-printing table). One screen is needed per colour, but there is no limit to the total number nor to their size, other than practicality. Beginning as a hand technique, where the screen was lifted and moved along the fabric after each printing, the process became automated during the 1950s.

Automatic flat-bed screen-printing machines are now used throughout Europe. The fabric is gummed to an endless printing blanket, which moves it, one repeat at a time, along a conveyor belt. The squeegees, which are the same as those used for printing by hand, are operated automatically. A more novel machine employs a *magnet roll* system. Here the 'squeegee' is a metal bar which is drawn across the screen, taking the colour with it, by the movement of magnets under the blanket. This method virtually eliminates screen wear and the possibility of colour drag.

Silkscreen printing, like all the aforementioned methods, has made its own impact on design. It has allowed greater design versatility without financial risk. During the post-war period it enabled manufacturers to reproduce the work of renowned artists as short, exclu-, sive runs. It also helped to reduce the time between the introduction of a fashionable idea and its printing. In the 1960s the speeding of fashion change could be accommodated only by using screen printing. The ability of screens to print very large motifs encouraged a trend towards huge patterns. The motifs applied to dress fabrics were often larger than those found on furnishing prints. Ephemeral goods such as tee-shirts and tea towels bearing topical slogans and images became widespread because of screen printing.

ROTARY SCREEN PRINTING

Rotary screen printing is a continuous method which has improved upon the speed and efficiency of flat screens. Introduced in 1954, the machines began

RIGHT: *An automatic Buser flat-bed screen, machine-printing a traditional furnishing chintz. The unprinted fabric can be seen entering the machine at the far end before passing under each of twelve screens, one for each printing colour.*

BELOW: *The screen is lifted while the operative feeds in more colour from a jug of dye.*

to be popular in Europe and the United States in the early 1960s. They comprise a series of finely perforated flexible cylindrical nickel screens, one per printing colour. Their length is dictated by the width of the fabric and their circumference by the height of the design repeat. Dye is introduced inside the screen by means of a hollow tube running along its length. This tube also supports a flexible steel *doctor* blade, which acts as a squeegee by forcing the colour through the screen on to the cloth. An automatic bed carries the fabric beneath the screens at a faster rate than with flat-screen machines.

At Sanderson's printworks at Uxbridge a rotary screen machine can produce between 10,000 and 12,000 metres (11,000 to 13,000 yards) of furnishing fabric daily (during a nine-hour shift) and a flat-bed machine only 2000 metres (2200 yards) in the same time. (Other firms, producing patterns with smaller repeats, would have a faster output in the same time.) Rotary machines are quicker in production but originally took longer to set up. Experienced operatives have gained in speed so that the only disadvantage of rotary machines now is that they need a little more maintenance than flat screens. Both techniques create virtually indistinguishable results and neither one is more suitable for a particular type of design; speed and cost are the criteria which govern the choice of either one.

Overall, flat-screen machines tend to have less wastage as the fabric moves through them at a slower rate. They are also preferable for thicker materials as they are capable, if necessary, of giving a heavier than usual deposit of dye. The fashion for sleeping under patterned duvets has helped to perpetuate the use of huge screens measuring about 3 metres

(9.8 feet) square. Rotary screens can also print very wide fabrics; for carpets it is possible to print widths up to 200 inches (4.99 m) using the rotary method.

In the 1980s one or other screen technique can cater for most customer requirements. Screens can print designs containing up to twenty-one colours and can reproduce effects once only possible using woodblocks and copperplates. While there is little to rival silk screens in speed, quality and versatility, its products, in common with those of all the other printing methods mentioned in this book, have to undergo a lengthy finishing process before they are ready to be sold.

A rotary Stork machine from Amsterdam printing a ten-colour furnishing fabric. This machine, made by a major producer of rotary screen machines, can print up to twenty colours under the supervision of two operatives. After all the colours have been printed the fabric is drawn off the blanket and passes straight into a long hot-air drying cabinet.

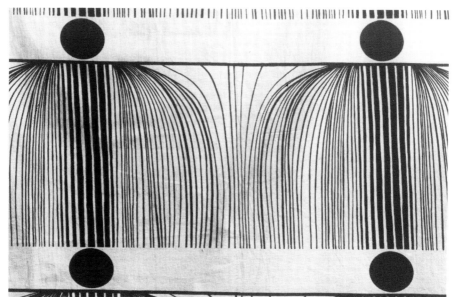

ABOVE: *'Caprice' designed by Barbara Brown, screen-printed by Heal Fabrics Ltd, London, as a 50 inch (1270 mm) wide furnishing cotton in 1964. The black on white geometric pattern, based on circles and stripes, is an early example of an 'op' art design.*

BELOW: *A furnishing fabric screen printed on 48 inch (1220 mm) fabric by Arthur Sanderson and Sons Ltd in 1968. The curved and pointed interlocking stripes in reds, pinks and orange, finely outlined in black on magenta cotton, reflect the late 1960s interest in Art Nouveau. The fashion for such large-scale abstract patterns could only be produced, at that time, using silkscreen.*

ABOVE: *Fabric being prepared for the Star steamer. The printed cloth is pinned, with a protective layer of plain fabric, around the star-like spokes of the frame. When full, the frame is placed on a trolley and wheeled into the steamer.*

RIGHT: *Once the steaming is completed the steamer rises automatically, the cloth is removed and, with the dyes now fixed, unwound from the frame ready to be washed.*

FINISHING

The colour of the cloth coming off the printing tables may bear little resemblance to the colour of the cloth when it leaves the factory. Once printed, the dyes must be fixed into the cloth, usually by exposure to steam. (The length of time can vary from a few minutes up to an hour according to the types of fabric, the dyes and the pressure and humidity levels in the steamer.) After steaming, unwanted chemicals are removed by a series of washes in cold water, followed by one in an almost boiling solution of detergent, to get rid of any remaining impurities. Drying and *stentering*, to straighten out the fabric's warp and weft, then take

27

place. If required, a *calender* machine, in which the fabric is passed between heated rotating metal cylinders, can be used to give a smooth surface finish to furnishing fabric. Resin is sometimes applied at this stage in order that furnishings should retain their smoothness, or to reduce shrinkage after washing and cleaning during use. Some types of resin can give flame retardation or provide flexible stiffness to fabrics intended for use as roller blinds. The amount of time necessary for finishing depends on the cloth and the colours used, but the process lengthens the printing time and adds to the cost of the final product.

NEW DEVELOPMENTS

New fabrics and the new technology have already stimulated changes in textile printing and will continue to do so. Post-war developments in the manufacture of synthetic fabrics such as cellulosics and polyesters have inspired and necessitated new ways of printing. One of the most noteworthy developments has been *sublimation* or *heat-transfer* printing, whereby paper is printed with dyes which can be vapourised and transferred to fabric held against the paper in the presence of heat. Introduced in the 1960s, this is a totally different technique to those already mentioned. Paper is printed with *subliming* or *disperse* dyes (suitable for polyesters, acrylics and other synthetics), which come into contact with the fabric for fifteen to twenty seconds at temperatures in excess of 200 Celsius. Designs consisting of up to eight colours, with three tones of each, can be printed in this way.

The technique is a more sophisticated

A Stork proofing press, shown producing a heat-transfer printed fabric. The printed paper and the polyester fabric enter the machine from separate rolls at the front, and heat is then applied evenly on a horizontal bed. The printed fabric comes out on a roll at the back, separate from the paper, which, having transferred the design, is discarded as waste. Larger-scale machines are used in industry but the same principle applies.

ABOVE: *The reverse of a heat-transfer print showing that the design does not penetrate the cloth. Without the second printing of a plain colour or a texture on the underside, the technique is unsuitable for textiles used for items such as curtains, where both sides will be visible when in use.*

BELOW: *A heat-transfer printed design of 1984 showing accuracy and detail which can rival the fineness of image found in printed books or magazines.*

A gravure machine, printing heat-transfer paper with six colours. The printing cylinders are made of copper-faced steel, which is engraved and then chrome plated for greater durability. Engraving is either carried out photographically or by using a computer-based electronic engraving machine. Each unit of the machine prints a different colour and the paper passes into the overhead drier between colour applications.

version of that which has been used over many years for embroidery transfers. It is very quick when compared with earlier methods, for the fabrics are ready to leave the factory as soon as the design has been transferred. The absence of the finishing process makes this method particularly suitable for knitted fabrics, which are liable to change shape during washing and drying. Commercially, heat transfer is only suitable for fabrics containing a high percentage of polyester, the higher the better for clarity of design. Pure white cloth is also preferable for the best colour reproduction. Unlike the aforementioned chemical processes, the pigment adheres to the surface of the cloth rather than being absorbed into it. Thus a heat-transfer print can usually be distinguished by examining the wrong side of the fabric.

Heat-transfer printing is not in direct competition with silkscreen work and cannot produce the same colour range, but it is a quick, clean, dry method which requires a relatively small initial investment and can be operated by semi-skilled workers. There is virtually no limitation to the designs that can be produced. It is especially suitable for extremely accurate and intricate patterns such as plaids and geometrics.

The patterning of, for example, polyester bedding has been made possible by the transfer of patterns from paper which can be up to 12 feet (3.65 m) wide. As synthetic fabrics are becoming more common, heat-transfer printing has a great deal of potential for the future. In 1984 Bemrose Transfer Prints of Derby increased their large exports of printed transfer paper to China, which has in-

30

vested heavily in polyester fabric manufacture.

Printing methods commonly used in the paper and packaging industries are applicable to transfer papers. *Gravure,* that is printing from engraved cylinders, gives the highest quality pattern reproduction. Computer-based electronic engraving machines now make it possible to attain a higher than ever degree of definition.

The impact of the new technology is not restricted to certain areas of textile printing. In direct printing, the preparation of colours can now be totally controlled by computer. By reading the colours required, a computer can estimate the constituent dyes and binders and their required proportions. The dyehouse of old, bearing the colourful traits of its purpose, has been transformed into a clean and healthy environment.

Many of the latest technological developments come from Japan. In 1977 the Japanese designer Issey Miyake combined with a Japanese dye printer to invent a method of printing cotton using a laser beam. The result was a beautiful geometrical pattern of subtly graduated colours. In the west the application of such technology is far less sophisticated and advanced. Two hundred years after textile printing began in earnest in Europe, innovation is once again coming from the east.

Fabric passing out of the steamer at Sanderson's Uxbridge factory.

PLACES TO VISIT

GREAT BRITAIN
Victoria and Albert Museum, Cromwell Road, South Kensington, London SW7 2RL. Telephone: 01-589 6371.
Whitworth Art Gallery. University of Manchester, Whitworth Park, Manchester M15 6ER. Telephone: 061-273 4865.
William Morris Gallery and Brangwyn Gift, Water House, Lloyd Park, Forest Road, Walthamstow, London E17 4PP. Telephone: 01-527 5544, extension 390.

FRANCE
Musee de l'Impression sur Etoffes, 3 Rue des Bonnes Gens, Mulhouse, Alsace. A unique musuem devoted entirely to textile printing, with a very full display both of techniques and of printed textiles.

FURTHER READING

Knecht, E. and Fothergill, J. B. *The Principles and Practice of Textile Printing*. Charles Griffin, 1912 to 1952. A very detailed, now out-of-date handbook.
Storey, J. *The Thames and Hudson Manual of Textile Printing*. Thames and Hudson, 1974. A useful manual giving a broad historical overview.
Robinson, S. *A History of Printed Textiles*. Studio Vista, 1969. A survey of worldwide developments.
Turnbull, G. *A History of the Calico Printing Industry of Great Britain*. Sherratt, Altrincham, 1951. A full history, with tables, which is worth reading despite some inaccuracies.

ACKNOWLEDGEMENTS
The author gratefully acknowledges the advice given by : Mr J. Greenwood, Mr K. Payne and staff at Arthur Sanderson and Sons Ltd. The photographs on the following pages are acknowledged to : Barrack Fabric Printing Company, Macclesfield, 21, 27; Bemrose (UK) Ltd, Derby, 28, 29, 30; Crafts Study Centre, Holburne Museum, Bath, 16; David Evans and Company, Crayford, Kent, cover, 2, 9, 14; Carol Mackenzie Gale, 13 (upper), 15 (lower), 22; Greater Manchester Museum of Science and Industry, 13 (lower); Manchester City Library, Archives, 19 (lower); William Morris Gallery, Walthamstow, 10, 15 (upper); Arthur Sanderson and Sons Ltd, 23, 25, 31; Victoria and Albert Museum (Crown Copyright), 3, 4(left), 5, 6, 8; Whitworth Art Gallery, Manchester, 1, 4 (right), 7, 18(lower), 24, 26.